DreamKeepers
Volume 2
Flight to Starfall

Story and Artwork by

VIVID
Independent Publishing.

DEDICATED TO
MARY RUNYAN

Throughout our most difficult times,
you have had the strength to push us onward.
This book would not have been possible without you.

Independent Publishing.

DreamKeepers and all subsidiary characters, concepts, and
material are copyright © 2005 - 2008 to David Lillie.

Fonts used courtesy of: blambot.com (ANIME ACE), Cumberland Fontworks (Cup and Talon),
Harold's Fonts (SOLEMNITY), Larabie Fonts (Vinque), the Scriptorium (STONECROSS), and
dafont.com (Celticmd, SAMDANEVIL, ZOMBIE, Minangkabau, BEAST WARS, KonQa, SHOGUNS
CLAN, DISTORTIA, LIITU, Potato Press, SCURLOCK, COMIC BOOK, BURRITO, DEKTER TERROR,
SUITRIBE, DALEK, BADABOOM BB, CRACKED JOHNNIE, DWARVEN STONECRAFT, ANGRYBLUE).
If any fonts used in this book have inaccurate or overlooked sources, please inform the pub-
lisher and credit will be issued in consecutive editions.

ISBN 0-9786990-1-7
Copyright © 2005-2008 by David Lillie.
All rights reserved. Printed in the U.S.A.

DreamKeepers Volume 2: Flight to Starfall
Published by Vivid Publishing 2008
General concept created by David Lillie and Brad Higginbotham.

Forward

There have been revolutionary changes behind the book. Working on 'Volume 2' of the *DreamKeepers* saga has been an exciting, challenging, and drastically different experience...

'Volume 1' was completed under contract with a different publisher, and with a different partner. Excited by the acceptance of an established graphic novel company, we eagerly awaited publication of the finished book... But it was not to be.

The publisher wanted the book's direction cleaned up, altered, cocked, and aimed directly at a lucrative child audience. After all, it was a *cartoon* book, right? Changes were called for. While expecting these devolutions to take place, the publisher discarded the release date, set the project on the back burner, and turned off the oven. Hungry to continue creating story regardless of business delays, I pushed forward on *DreamKeepers* - and was dragged to a grinding halt by my counterpart. Hoping and prodding for my partner to carry his end of the creative process, I watched days turn to weeks, weeks slide into months, and the months form a bleak stack.

I may be young, but I'm not complacent. Determined to bring *DreamKeepers* to the world with its vision and integrity intact, I broke away from the short-sighted old publishing company. With no money and no connections, I created Vivid Publishing to forge ahead with *DK*. Likewise, the withered standstill on creativity direly needed a shot of life - even if I had no choice but to provide it alone. I finally began contributing to the lagging areas of the project.

This renewed direction was far from appreciated, and regretfully things settled with the conclusion of both a partnership and a friendship.

The publication process for 'Volume 1' was jumpstarted despite opposition, freeing the story to grow, live, and move forward. Without the fear of bruising feelings, the book was gratefully able to undergo revising and polishing prior to release.

It was a colossal relief to at last be free of restraint, and see the ocean of creativity spread before me with no barriers. Nonexistent backstories, half-finished characters, and story arcs all awaited fulfillment and flair. No longer obliged to force the storyline through an inert filter, the ease of writing and creating was shockingly refreshing. With careful focus and effort, the DreamWorld began to grow and glint. But as fortune would have it, I was not destined to labor alone after all.

Bouncing ideas off my fiancée-to-be Liz proved to be increasingly valuable as the writing revitalized. The quintessential devil's advocate, her incisive questions and insights brought thought and attention into unexpectedly essential aspects of character and story. As *DreamKeepers* awakened in scope and richness, so did our working relationship. This was far different from an obligatory collaboration constrained by bonds of friendship. Rather, working with Liz has become a natural union of actively creative talents, accenting and amplifying one another. At this point, I must acknowledge that *DreamKeepers* has finally found the team it was meant for, as the Volume in your hands will illustrate.

Not that our accomplishments have been effortless. In a world dominated by massive corporations and addicted to soulless mass media, it's hard to start with nothing but passion. The creative challenges are formidable as well - it is no simple task mass-producing pages of artwork with such exacting standards. The closing months of work on this book were completed in a relentless nocturnal haze, sustained by a surreal blend of coffee and KMFDM. But in the end reality was brushed aside, and determination prevailed.

Here it is - the complete second volume of the *DreamKeepers* saga. Crafted at the unlikely crossroads of unrestrained creative freedom and meticulous, caretaking execution, what you hold before you now is a rare thing indeed. Thank you for finding this book, and consider this your formal invitation to explore the story within... Picking up where the last book left off, a winding tale of color, adventure, intrigue, and danger awaits. So find a seclusive and special place to secret yourself, curl up with a favorite drink and a bright lamp, and enjoy the story.

David Lillie

There are more to come.

Overview: the Third War of Anduruna

To relate a comprehensive historical account of the 'Third War of Anduruna' (Ia), one must document its origins, down to the most minute aspect. It is interesting to note that, in light of its catastrophic proportions, the great conflict of our time unfolded innocuously within the lives of a handful of unsuspecting young DreamKeepers.

Two such youths were Mace and Whip (Ib) of the Margate district's orphanage dock-yards. Without warning, during a violently storming night, their younger companion Paige was brutally slaughtered by a minion of the nightmare hordes.

It must be remembered that this was a time when the existence of the nightmares was mere myth to the Andurunans, as the foul creatures had been in hiding for generations. As such, murder was the only conceivable explanation for the young girl's horrific death - with Mace being blamed as the culprit.

That same bloody night, portentous occurrences also involved Tinsel Nanaja, the fashion celebrity turned political councilor to the Viscount. (Ic) Her complicity in a jealous murder plot was overheard by one of the Viscount's daughters, Namah Calah. (Id) Reacting quickly, Tinsel attacked both Namah and her half-sister Lilith the next morning, in a secluded room of the Tower. Unaware of how to use their powers at that time (Ie), the girls nevertheless managed to escape, and took refuge with their estranged fugitive uncle, Igrath Winters. (If)

As fate would conspire, Mace and Whip were taken to Igrath's that same day, in relation to the dock incident. Their paths inextricably crossed, the four young DreamKeepers found rest - believing their ordeals had ended.

By no feat of imagination could they have predicted the great and tragic events immi-nent. Through no act of their own, these DreamKeepers were to become a fulcrum of chaos and turmoil - epicenters of the unholy maelstrom destined to engulf the known DreamWorld, altering it forever.

-Nainso Ziska II, Esq.

Tinsel

Mace & Whip

Namah

Lilith

Igrath

(Ia) Note that this phrase is the most commonly applied title for the latest Nightmare War, despite not in actuality being the third conflict to occur in the Anduruna territory. This title fails to acknowledge the 'Toll Wars' and the 'Last War of Powers', the civil conflict which ensued several generations after the repulsion of the Extollo.

(Ib) Mace and Whip (no last name available) have additional background information, scant though it may be, recorded in the biographies addendum (b.a.) to this text.

(Ic) At the time her affiliation was unsuspected to all but a select few, although she became notorious in later times for various heinous actions committed as a Dark DreamKeeper.

(Id) See the b.a. - although secreted from the public view, Namah Calah was indeed an illegitimate child to the Viscount.

(Ie) Any and all Power use had been outlawed in Anduruna at this time, ostensibly for the safety of the public. Even a rudimentary awareness and training in one's innate abilities was inaccessible to the citizens of that era.

(If) The same Igrath Winters who was at one time captain of the city guard, and later turned fugitive from justice. An extensive history is available in the b.a.

Chapter 4

Forgotten Fortress

Chapter 5

Pawns Dispatch

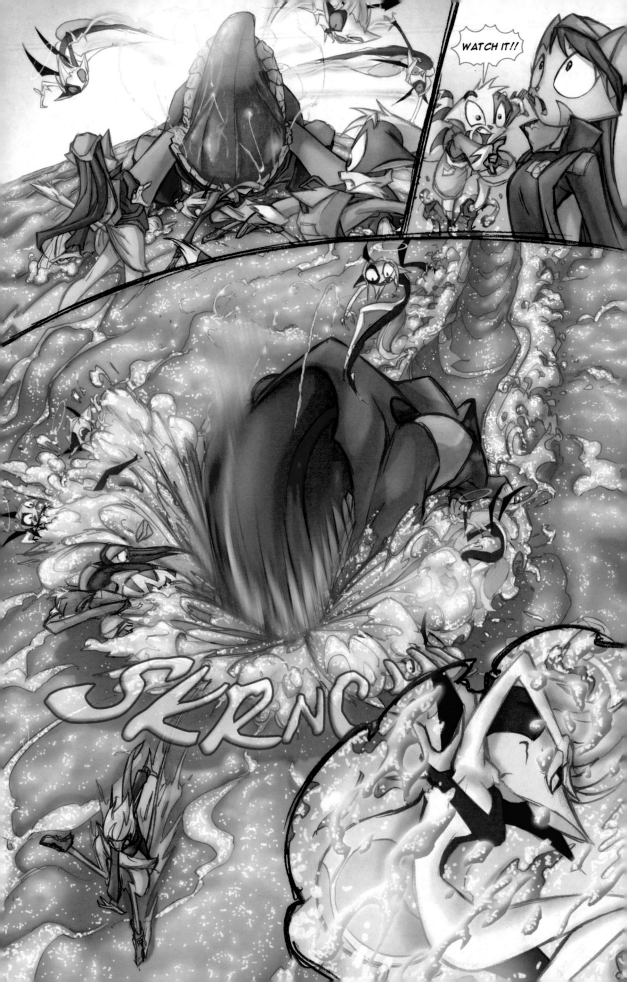

GRAAAUUGH!

DAMNIIIT!

JUST WHAT DO YOU THINK THEY'RE DOING OVER THERE?

SMILEY! SMILEY! RUN!

Chapter 6

Restoration Unveiled

The End

of

Volume 2

Harvest Festival

Without exception, the Harvest Festival was the most raucously celebrated holiday Anduruna recognized. Although its ancient roots are lost, the name of the festival, combined with the season, may offer us a faint hint as to the ritual's origin. Although it began as a wholesome feast in recognition and enjoyment of a good year's work, the contemporary affair bore almost zero resemblance to the time - honored tradition. The pre-war Andurunan Harvest Festival was a blaring, bazaar - like romp, a gluttonous consumption of wanton excess in every form. While I have fond memories of indulging select of my own predilections during these times, these notations are for posterity, and as such I shall elaborate instead on some of the common customs inherent to the celebration.

Beads: In addition to excessive eating (and excessive drinking), beads were a staple of Harvest Festival activity. They were given out for hundreds of different reasons - ranging from innocent and carefree to appallingly decadent. The intended purpose for giving a bead was displayed in its design and color - there were dozens of recognized symbol and color combinations, in addition to customized beads used by various subcultures. Bead vendors would set up shop during the festival to sell their wares - so, depending on one's taste, DreamKeepers would purchase their beads of choice, and go carousing.

Jester Beads: Orange in coloration, these beads were gifted in recognition of any good joke or occasion for hilarity.

Venus Beads: tokens of gratitude for affection shown - pink for tender innocence and kisses, and scarlet for bawdier fare.

Mystic Beads: Indigo in tone, these beads are given to artful performers and magicians, who use the beads to advertise their prowess throughout the rest of the year.

Bravado Beads: For those seeking entertainment at another's expense, these green trinkets are bestowed in return for dares fulfilled.

Beads could be purchased individually, or by the string. Some of the most universal bead designs are shown at left.

Necklaces: Spiral necklaces were the favorite way to store beads collected during the holiday. When the festivities concluded, the necklace served as a visual portrait of the celebration, displaying the various personal undertakings of the owner. Beaded necklaces from years past were often conversation pieces of their owners, and could tickle the memory as effectively as any image album.

Costuming: Although dramatic attire had always been a traditional part of the festival, the allure of anonymity certainly had its role in encouraging the continuation of the practice. Originally refined to nightmarish or horrific subjects, in later generations costuming expanded wildly to include any outlandish garb, especially feminine attire ill suited to the time of year.

Shock Troopers

In a society wherein power use was rigidly outlawed, a means had to be established to enforce this directive - among others. When Anduruna needed to suppress, detain, or eliminate any fractious element of its population, it deployed only the finest.

Firepower: illustrated left is the standard issue cylinder-loaded full bore springer-rifle. Cartridges are speed-loaded into the firing chamber and severed - loosing the hyper-compressed spring, and launching a heavy-nose carbonite projectile through the air. Fired rounds are designed for maximum penetration value, able to skewer through several feet of conventional masonry. The loose spring is auto-ejected from the side slats, instantly clearing the barrel for another round.

Tipping every rifle is a 'door-buster'. using an alternate trigger, a compression mechanism inside delivers a massive concussion to any contacting surface.

Every trooper has an ID badge on their uniform which serves as their virtual passcard to secure areas, and transmits their location & status to their teammates HUD goggles. Additionally, missing suits can be flagged and tracked using the ID badge, making uniform theft or impersonation impossible.

Spare cartridge cylinders are secured to the belt.

Shock troopers were culled from the ranks of standard law enforcement based upon qualities such as loyalty, bravery under fire, professionalism, and most importantly, protocol. Their regimen included rigorous and constant conditioning, comprehensive armed and unarmed combat training, and the development of involuntary tactical reflexes.
However, the physical aspect of their training was only the beginning. Rote memorization of laws and regulations by the hundreds, mental conditioning to view all citizens as potential 'infractors', encouraging thoughts of ultimate authority serving the ultimate public good, positive reinforcement for unblinking obedience, and implanting a distinct negative connation with hesitation or second thoughts all served to make the shock troopers a powerful and dispassionate service to the authorities - and as effective and uncaring as the tools of their trade.

...The public was told they were 'safety' troops.

Designed to facilitate an overwhelming fusillade, this overlapping formation affords maximum firepower combined with near total armor coverage.

Secondary armaments include toys such as the extendible riot control stick - its weighted tip can crush bone with a well placed blow. A throwing knife with a knuckle-guard completes the ensemble.

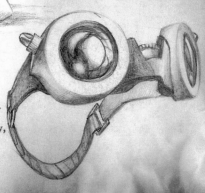

The FullScan HUD goggles are standard issue to every trooper. Their digitized display indicates updated directives, waypoints, and the locations of friendly units. The HUDs are also designed to scan multiple spectrums of visibility, allowing troopers to see through smoke or haze, in total darkness, and even pick up on body-heat signatures through the walls of buildings.

In 'cover position', a fully armored shock trooper can withstand even explosive assaults nearly intact.

Groundcars

The need for an individual mode of transportation was precluded in such a centralized society as Anduruna. Shipping was facilitated by coastal docks and the Eridan River, while prevalent public transportation was afforded by tolled watercars in the Calypsan aqueduct system. Especially with the integration of the Tower Teleportation Service in latter years, groundcars were the least prevalent form of transportation used. However, they could still be seen carting through the streets from time to time. Although unnecessary, flashy overpriced groundcars were a favorite toy for the rich to parade. And, of course, the shock troops had need for a versatile means of deployment.

Beasts: Technological progress favoring more necessary areas of focus such as entertainment, groundcars remained a biologically propelled device. Beasts of burden common to the task included the knossus, illustrated left. Powerful, docile, and easily trained, the knossus was perfect for military transport. Huge sums were wasted trying to develop armor for the creatures, but their natural resilience outperformed all artificial protections - no matter how much tax money was spent. In fact, trained knossus were used to destroy barricades and blockades before the 'door-busters' became standard issue for shock troops.

Knossus
(näs´əs)

Pictured above, a trained knossus is carting a Shock-Trooper Combat Deployment Groundcar - or, as they were publicly termed, 'friend rollers'. The combat car was equipped with solid rubber tires and a five-inch thick multi-layer honeycomb armor plating. Firing slots in the walls transformed the car into a mobile war-station, nearly impervious to return fire. To allow maximum troop mobility, the combat car had additional armored cover incorporated into its design. The benches could be disengaged and pulled out on sliding racks, to be deployed as mobile barricades on the field.

Manekale (manɔ̄ kāl)
(male - 4th horn on muzzle)

Kerrick
(kar´ik)

Manekales: More economic to care for than the massive knossus, manekales were the common beasts of burden. Useful for hauling anything from carts to groundcars, manekales were often rented from city ranching operations, circumventing ownership cost. Additionally, manekales were essential for anyone wishing to journey out into the wilderness beyond Anduruna - although, due to the commonality of no return, renting an animal for this purpose was out of the question. Kerricks were often used for quick trips or deliveries, due to their speed, despite being incapable of bearing heavy loads. The single backswept horn of the kerrick made for hilariously easy steering.

Luxury Groundcars: Featured right is one of the more expensive models of luxury groundcar that were popular among celebrities and the rich. The horn was considered one of the most vital adornments, as it allowed one to let fly a derisive squawk at less fortunate citizens on foot. As a personal note, I suspect that the formation of a society which aspires to the tastelessly insipid aesthetics of these... pods... ensured that, were fate in wavering indecision, the scales would be tipped and cataclysm unleashed upon the DreamWorld.

Production Samples

More than imagination went into the fantastic cliffs and waterfalls of this book. Camera equipped and shooting for inspiration, Liz and I had the pleasure of exploring the majestic Hocking Hills region of Ohio together in the summer leading up to Volume 2's inception. The sweeping vistas, perpetual twilight gorges, hidden caves, and cascading curtains of water contributed powerfully to the art, although their intrinsic natural impact cannot truly be captured by pencil or camera.

The dappled sunlight added so much atmosphere and depth to the landscapes - I tried to recapture this effect in some scenes, but the original sensation was indelibly unique.

Of the photos I took, the image to the left is my favorite; it begins to express the sheer scale and awe of the environment. The specks in the back are people.

After a hot summer afternoon of hiking, tempting forest pools proved to be exquisitely refreshing. So refreshing, my glasses were cast into the depths by an exuberant head-dunk. I waded intently throughout the area, reflecting upon how much easier the search would be if I had my glasses. The elusive spectacles were retrieved by our good friend Laura's toes, serendipitously, while she was dodging fish.

After dunking and wading for some time, I realized that it would have been a good idea to remove Liz's digital camera from my pocket first. Remarkably, the drenched electronic device returned to perfect working order after it dried out.

Production Samples

Swatch Sheets - To make sure the precisely right colors match the right characters, swatch sheets are used. An extra sheet was drafted for the main characters in Volume 2, to track the clothing cohesion of their winter - gear costume change.

The color choices from the swatch sheets guide the color blocking process, which involves laying out the color scheme and tone placement of each setting. Below is an example the intricate and time consuming work that goes into the color blocking.

The line work style of DK diverges from the inked technique of traditional comics. Pencil work grants a subtle texture to the drawing, reminiscent of traditional rough animation, and hinting at the simple paper and pencil foundation of the visuals.

This textured line quality makes the color blocking far more than a simple click-and-fill job. Each shape of color must be meticulously hand selected and painted digitally, using an artistic tact in interpreting the subtle detailing of the pencil sketch.

About the Author-Artists

David Lillie and Liz Thomas grew up in Michigan, and met for the first time attending art school. David graduated in 2005, and Liz in '07. After collaborating on several freelance animation jobs, they founded Vivid Publishing together; Dave and Liz are currently working in tandem on the DreamKeepers graphic novel saga. Midway through production of this book Dave and Liz became engaged and are looking forward to their wedding. Below, they share some personal notes about one another:

Liz sports a set of sharp green eyes which have proven remarkably adept at noting and correcting the slew of mistakes left in the wake of my drawing sprees. Her bright blonde hair doesn't have a specific function, but it doesn't hurt to look at. Anyone foolish enough to try taking advantage of her pleasant demeanor will typically find themselves stumbling unwittingly into the crosshairs of a hidden feisty streak a mile wide.

When not nurturing her vintage music collection, she enjoys raising vicious predators. Notable favorites included praying mantids, and our disbelievingly outraged bonsai alligator.

-David

If one were to summarize **'David** Lillie'…with his dynamic energy, amiable charisma, and formidable perseverance…the word 'squirrelly' is unanimously popular with our cohorts. However, the parallels of tree-climbing and forgetting where he left things neglect to include his passion for swimming; his deceptively palatable culinary adventures dried on the stovetop; and the expert business logistics he shares during strolls about town.

Dave's appeal and boyish sincerity personify his gifted talents the way devouring adult literature by lamplight exempts the adornment of his fluffy doggy slippers.

-Liz

VIVID©
Independent Publishing.

Thank you for enjoying the book, and for supporting an independent publishing venture. To delve deeper into the DreamWorld, go online! The story continues - see Behind the Scenes for updates and production art on the next graphic novel. While you're visiting, enjoy *Prelude*, the free weekly web comic which features the childhood adventures of the DreamKeepers characters! This plus art galleries, contests, character profiles, reviews, interviews, and more!

www.dreamkeeperscomic.com